Name _____

Overall Assessment

Directions Name each polygon.

1.

2.

3.

4.

_____   _____   _____   _____

Directions Find the perimeter.

5.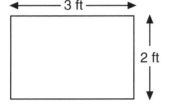
3 ft
2 ft

6.
15 m
8 m

7.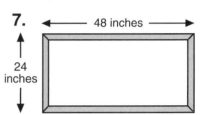
48 inches
24 inches

_____   _____   _____

Directions Name the circle and its parts. Use the figure at the right.

8. center _____

9. diameter _____

10. 3 radii _____

11. 2 chords _____

Figure A

Directions Find the circumference. Use 3.14 as π.

12.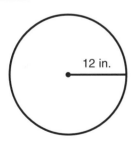
12 in.

13.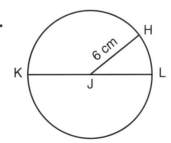
6 cm
H
K   L
J

14.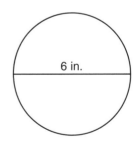
6 in.

_____   _____   _____

Go on to the next page.

Name _____   Date _____

Overall Assessment, p. 2

Directions Find the area.

15.

8 m

_____

16.
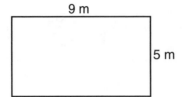
9 m
5 m

_____

17.
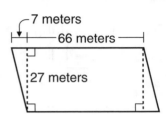
7 meters
66 meters
27 meters

_____

18.
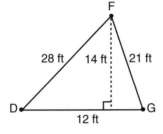
F
28 ft   14 ft   21 ft
D
12 ft
G

_____

19.
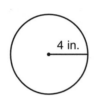
4 in.

_____

20.
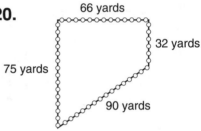
66 yards
32 yards
75 yards
90 yards

_____

Directions Use the figure to answer 21–24.

21. The area of the square is _____.

22. The area of the circle is _____.

23. The radius of the circle is _____.

24. The area of the shaded region is _____.

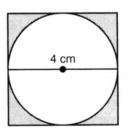
4 cm

Directions Solve.

25. Vanessa's room is 15 feet long and 12 feet wide.

    What is the area of her room? _____

    Carpet costs $11.95 per square yard.

    What would be the cost to carpet Vanessa's room? _____

Name _____ Date _____

Unit 1 Assessment

Directions Use the figure to answer 1–4.

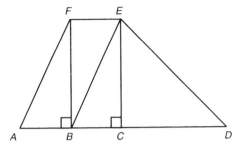

1. Name a rectangle. _____

2. Name a parallelogram that is not a rectangle.

_____

3. Name 3 triangles. _____

4. Name 3 trapezoids. _____

Directions Find the perimeter.

5.

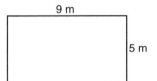

9 m

5 m

_____

6.

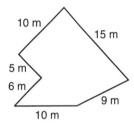

10 m
15 m
5 m
6 m
9 m
10 m

_____

Directions Find the circumference. Use 3.14 as π.

7. $d = 4$ cm

_____

8. $r = 100$ m

_____

9. $d = 7$ ft

_____

10. $r = 5\frac{1}{2}$ in.

_____

Directions Find the area.

11.

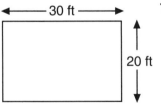

30 ft

20 ft

_____

12.

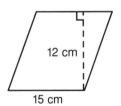

12 cm

15 cm

_____

13.

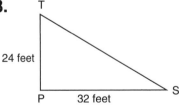

T

24 feet

P   32 feet   S

_____

Polygons

A **polygon** is a figure made up of line segments. Its sides meet to form angles.

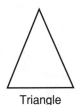
Triangle

Quadrilateral

Pentagon

Hexagon

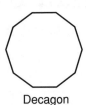
Octagon

Decagon

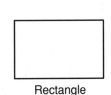
Parallelogram

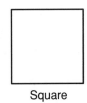
Rectangle

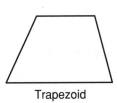
Square

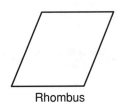
Trapezoid

Rhombus

Directions Name the polygon.

1.

_____

2.

_____

Directions Name the quadrilaterals.

3.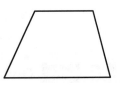

_____

4.

_____

Directions Which polygons below are

5. trapezoids?

_____

6. squares?

_____

7. rectangles?

_____

8. parallelograms?

_____

a.

b.

c.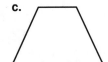

d.

e.

f.

Name That Polygon

Names are given to **polygons** according to the number of sides and the number of angles they have.

In a **regular polygon**, all the sides are congruent and all of the angles are congruent.

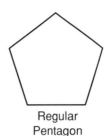
Regular
Pentagon

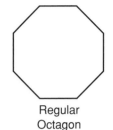
Regular
Octagon

Directions Is it a regular polygon? Write *yes* or *no*.

1.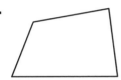
_____

2.
_____

3.
_____

4.
_____

5.
_____

6.
_____

7.
_____

8.
_____

Directions Is it a regular polygon? Write *yes* or *no*. If *yes*, name the polygon.

9.
_____

10.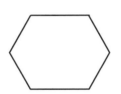
_____

11.
_____

12.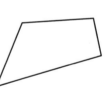
_____

13.
_____

14.
_____

15.
_____

16.
_____

Name _____ Date _____

Polygons and Their Characteristics

	Name	Figure	Description	Complete.
1.	Trapezoid	W, X, Z, Y	A quadrilateral with only 1 pair of parallel sides.	$\overline{WX}$ ∥ _____
2.	Parallelogram	L, M, P, N	Opposite sides are parallel and congruent.	$\overline{LM}$ ∥ _____ $\overline{MN}$ ∥ _____ $\overline{LM}$ ≅ _____ $\overline{MN}$ ≅ _____
3.	Rhombus	S, T, W, V	A parallelogram with 4 congruent sides	$\overline{ST}$ ≅ _____ ≅ _____ ≅ _____
4.	Rectangle	A, B, D, C	A parallelogram that has 4 right angles	m∠A = _____° m∠B = _____° m∠C = _____° m∠D = _____°
5.	Square	J, K, M, L	A rectangle that has 4 congruent sides	$\overline{JK}$ ≅ _____ ≅ _____ ≅ _____

Directions Use the figure at the right for 6–8.

6. Name a rectangle. _____

7. Name a parallelogram that is not a rectangle.

_____

8. Name 3 trapezoids. _____

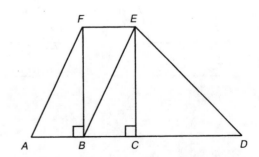

Name _____ Date _____

Quadrilateral Relationships

Name	Description
Quadrilateral	Polygon with 4 sides
Trapezoid	Quadrilateral with only 1 pair of parallel sides
Parallelogram	Quadrilateral with opposite sides parallel and congruent
Rectangle	Parallelogram with 4 right angles
Square	Rectangle with all sides congruent
Rhombus	Parallelogram with all sides congruent

Directions For each figure, circle each name that can be used to describe it.

1.

quadrilateral   rectangle
parallelogram   square
trapezoid   rhombus

2.

quadrilateral   rectangle
parallelogram   square
trapezoid   rhombus

3.

quadrilateral   rectangle
parallelogram   square
trapezoid   rhombus

4.

quadrilateral   rectangle
parallelogram   square
trapezoid   rhombus

5.

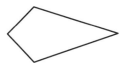

quadrilateral   rectangle
parallelogram   square
trapezoid   rhombus

6.

quadrilateral   rectangle
parallelogram   square
trapezoid   rhombus

Name _____ Date _____

Perimeter of Polygons

The **perimeter** of a figure is the sum of the lengths of the sides. Add to find the perimeter of this rectangle.

$$\begin{array}{r} 15 \\ 26 \\ 15 \\ +\ 26 \\ \hline \mathbf{82} \end{array}$$

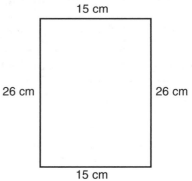

The perimeter is 82 centimeters.

Directions Find the perimeter of each polygon.

1.

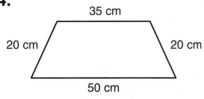

_____

2.

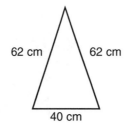

_____

3.

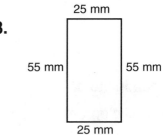

_____

4.

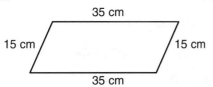

_____

5.

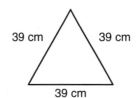

_____

6.

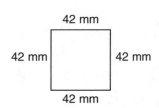

_____

7.

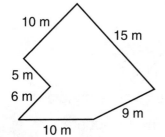

_____

8.

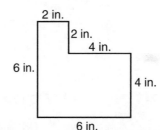

_____

9.

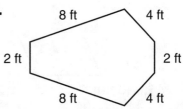

_____

Name _____   Date _____

Perimeter Formulas

The distance around a polygon is its **perimeter**. These are the formulas for the perimeter of a triangle, a rectangle, and a square.

   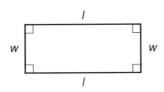

$$P = a + b + c \qquad\qquad P = 2l + 2w \qquad\qquad P = 4s$$

| **Directions** Find the perimeter of each polygon. |

1. 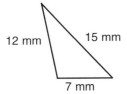   **2.**   **3.**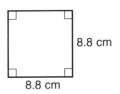

_____   _____   _____

| **Directions** Find the perimeter of a triangle when |

4. $a = 6.4$ cm, $b = 14.7$ cm, and $c = 17.5$ cm. _____

5. $a = 3.25$ m, $b = 4.56$ m, and $c = 5.29$ m. _____

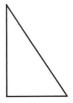

| **Directions** Find the perimeter of a rectangle when |

6. $l = 54$ cm and $w = 36$ cm. _____

7. $l = 4.9$ m and $w = 6.6$ m. _____

8. $l = 71.3$ cm and $w = 59.9$ cm. _____

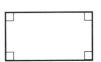

| **Directions** Find the perimeter of a square when |

9. $s = 128$ cm. _____   **10.** $s = 8.2$ m. _____

11. $s = 27.4$ cm. _____   **12.** $s = 6.7$ m. _____

Circles

In **circle** C, $\overline{AC}$, $\overline{CB}$ and $\overline{CD}$ are **radii**.

$\overline{AB}$ is a **diameter**.

$\overline{EF}$ and $\overline{AB}$ are **chords**.

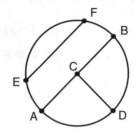

Directions Answer the questions using Figure A.

1. What is the name of this circle? _____

2. Name 2 chords of this circle. _____

3. How long is radius $\overline{PQ}$? _____

4. How long is radius $\overline{PN}$? _____

5. How long is diameter $\overline{NQ}$? _____

6. How long would another radius for this circle be? _____

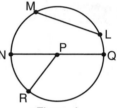

Figure A

Directions Answer the questions using Figure B.

7. Name the circle. _____

8. Name 3 radii. _____

9. Name 3 chords. _____

10. Name an acute angle. _____

11. Name an obtuse angle. _____

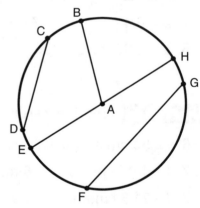

Figure B

Name _____   Date _____

Circumference of Circles

You can think of circumference in these ways:

1. Distance around the outside of a circle
You will need an aluminum can, some string, and scissors.

- Cut a length of string equal to the circumference of the can.
- Cut a second length of string equal to the diameter of the top of the can.
- Compare the lengths of the 2 strings.
- How many times longer is the circumference string than the diameter string?

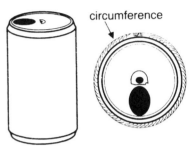

_____

2. The formula for circumference is pi × diameter ($C = \pi \times d$).

- How long is the diameter of the aluminum can? _____
- Multiply that length by π (use 3.14 or $\frac{22}{7}$). _____
- Is the circumference of the can close to that number? _____

Directions Find each circumference. Use 3.14 for π.

3.

3 in.

_____

4.

20 cm

_____

5.
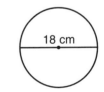
18 cm

_____

Directions Find each circumference. Use $\frac{22}{7}$ for π.

6.

21 in.

_____

7.

14 mm

_____

8.

9 in.

_____

Name _____   Date _____

Diameter and Radius

To find the circumference of a circle, find the radius or the diameter and multiply by pi.

If you know the radius, use $C = 2\pi r$.
[The radius is half of the diameter, so it needs to be doubled.]

If you know the diameter, use $C = \pi d$.

Directions Find the circumference. Use 3.14 for π.

1.
3 m

2.
12 cm

3.
18 mm

_____   _____   _____

4. diameter = 4 cm

5. diameter = 9 in.

6. radius = 15 m

_____   _____   _____

Directions Find the circumference. Use $\frac{22}{7}$ for π.

7. diameter = 14 in.

8. diameter = 42 mm

9. diameter = 28 cm

_____   _____   _____

10. radius = 14 in.

11. radius = 7 cm

12. radius = 21 ft

_____   _____   _____

Areas of Rectangles and Squares

Area is the number of square units that cover a surface. Area is measured in square inches (in.^{2}), square feet (ft^2), square meters (m^2), and so on.

Area of Rectangles

To find the **area** of a rectangle, multiply the length times the width.

$A = l \times w$

$A = 6 \times 3$

$A = 18$ cm^2

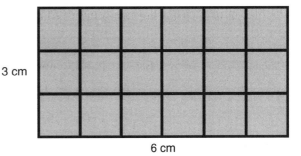

3 cm

6 cm

The area of the rectangle is 18 square centimeters.

To find the area of a square, multiply the side by itself.

$A = s \times s$ or $A = s^2$

$A = 3 \times 3$ or $A = 3^2$

$A = 9$ cm^2 $A = 9$ cm^2

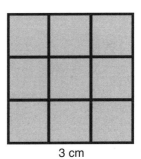

3 cm

3 cm

Directions **The length and the width are given. Find the area of each.**

1.
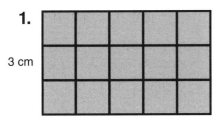

3 cm

5 cm

_____

2.
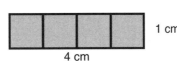

1 cm

4 cm

_____

3.
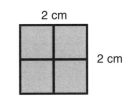

2 cm

2 cm

_____

4. $l = 7$ cm, $w = 3$ cm _____

5. $l = 8$ mm, $w = 4$ mm _____

6. $l = 9$ cm, $w = 5$ cm _____

7. $l = 12$ m, $w = 14$ m _____

8. $s = 6$ cm _____

9. $s = 8$ mm _____

10. $s = 2$ m _____

11. $s = 5$ m _____

Name _____ Date _____

Area of Parallelograms and Triangles

The **height** of a figure is the perpendicular distance from the base to the highest point. Height is part of the area formula for both parallelograms and triangles.

To find the area of a parallelogram, multiply the length of the base times the height.

$$A = b \times h$$

Replace the variables with numbers.

$A = 4 \times 3$
$A = 12 \text{ cm}^2$

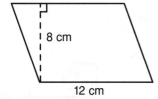

To find the area of a triangle, multiply $\frac{1}{2}$ times the length of the base times the height.

$$A = \frac{1}{2} \times b \times h$$

Replace the variables with numbers.

$A = \frac{1}{2} \times 4 \times 3$
$A = 6 \text{ cm}^2$

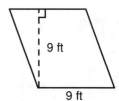

Directions Find the area of the parallelogram. Use the formula $A = b \times h$.

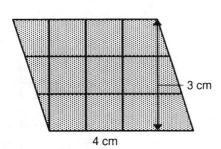

1.
8 cm
12 cm

$A =$ _____

2.
3 in.
10 in.

$A =$ _____

3.
9 ft
9 ft

$A =$ _____

Directions Find the area of the triangle. Use the formula $A = \frac{1}{2} \times b \times h$.

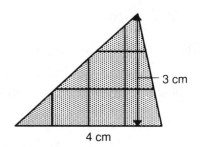

4.
6 cm
8 cm

$A =$ _____

5.
12 m
10 m

$A =$ _____

6.
6 in.
12 in.

$A =$ _____

Name _____ Date _____

Area

Directions Write the formula you would use to determine the area of each figure.

1.
square

_____

2.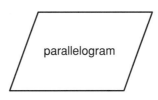
parallelogram

_____

3.
rectangle

_____

Directions Write the area of each square.

4.
4 m

_____

5.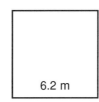
6.2 m

_____

6.
14.2 m

_____

Directions Write the area of each rectangle.

7.
12 mm
18.3 mm

_____

8.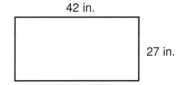
7.4 cm   0.85 cm

_____

9.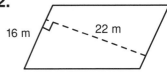
42 in.
27 in.

_____

Directions Write the area of each parallelogram.

10.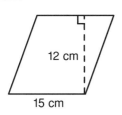
12 cm
15 cm

_____

11.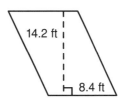
14.2 ft
8.4 ft

_____

12.
16 m   22 m

_____

Name _____ Date _____

Unit 2 Assessment

Directions Find the perimeter.

1.

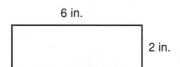

6 in.
2 in.

2.

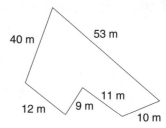

40 m
53 m
12 m
9 m
11 m
10 m

_____

_____

Directions Find the circumference. Use 3.14 as π.

3.

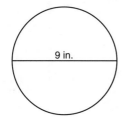

9 in.

4.

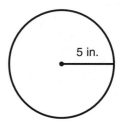

5 in.

_____

_____

Directions Find the area.

5.

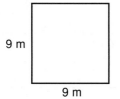

9 m
9 m

6.

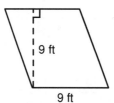

9 ft
9 ft

7.

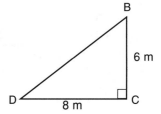

B
6 m
D
8 m
C

_____

_____

_____

8.

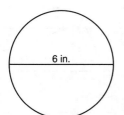

6 in.

9.

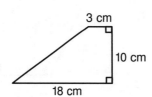

3 cm
10 cm
18 cm

10.

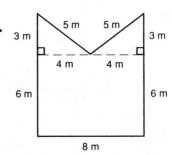

5 m   5 m
3 m   3 m
4 m   4 m
6 m   6 m
8 m

_____

_____

_____

Name _____ Date _____

Quadrilaterals

Some quadrilaterals have special names.

Trapezoid

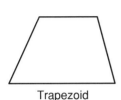

Parallelogram

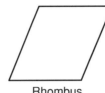

Rhombus

Rectangle

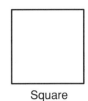

Square

Directions Classify each quadrilateral as a *trapezoid, parallelogram, rhombus, rectangle,* or *square*. List each name that applies to the figure.

1.

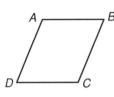

_____

_____

2.

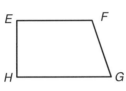

_____

_____

3.

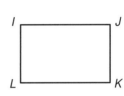

_____

_____

4.

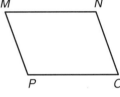

_____

_____

5.

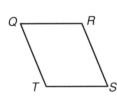

_____

_____

6.

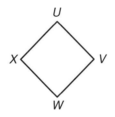

_____

_____

7.

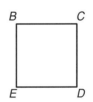

_____

_____

8.

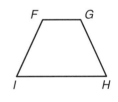

_____

_____

Directions Name the pairs of parallel sides in

9. figure *ABCD*.

_____

_____

10. figure *EFGH*.

_____

_____

11. figure *IJKL*.

_____

_____

12. figure *MNOP*.

_____

_____

13. figure *QRST*.

_____

_____

14. figure *UVWX*.

_____

_____

15. figure *BCDE*.

_____

_____

16. figure *FGHI*.

_____

_____

Name _____ Date _____

Estimating Perimeter

The **perimeter** of a figure is the sum of the lengths of the sides. Add to find the perimeter of this rectangle.

15
26
15
+ 26
82

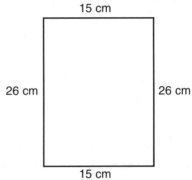

The perimeter is 82 centimeters.

Directions Find the perimeter of the polygon.

1.
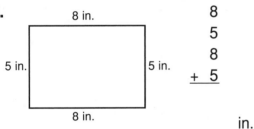

8
5
8
+ 5

_____ in.

2.
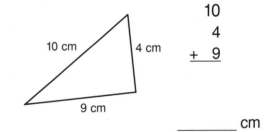

10
4
+ 9

_____ cm

3.
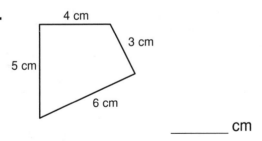

_____ cm

4.
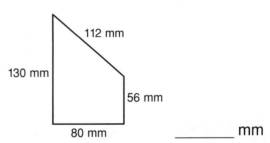

_____ mm

Directions Estimate the perimeter of the polygon. Round each length to the nearest whole number.

5.
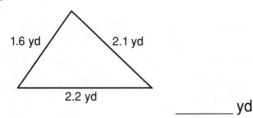

_____ yd

6.
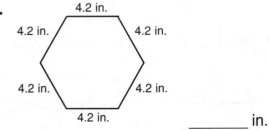

_____ in.

Perimeter of Polygons

The **perimeter** of a polygon is the sum of the lengths of its sides.

The formula for the
perimeter of a triangle is
$P = a + b + c$.

The formula for the
perimeter of a square is
$P = 4s$.

The formula for the
perimeter of a rectangle is
$P = 2l + 2w$.

Directions Find the perimeter of each polygon.

1.

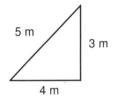

5 m   3 m   4 m

_____

2.

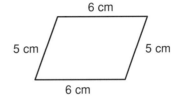

6 cm   5 cm   5 cm   6 cm

_____

3.

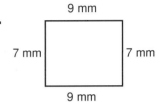

9 mm   7 mm   7 mm   9 mm

_____

4.

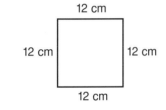

12 cm   12 cm   12 cm   12 cm

_____

5.

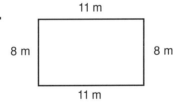

11 m   8 m   8 m   11 m

_____

Directions Find the perimeter of each regular polygon.

6.

19 mm

_____

7.

28 cm

_____

8.

4 m

_____

Name _____ Date _____

Add It Up

Remember: The perimeter of a figure is the sum of the lengths of the sides.

Directions Find the perimeter of each polygon.

1.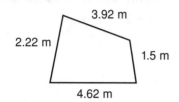

3.92 m

2.22 m

1.5 m

4.62 m

_____

2.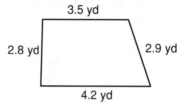

3.5 yd

2.8 yd

2.9 yd

4.2 yd

_____

3.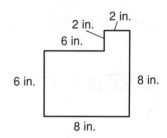

2 in.

2 in.

6 in.

6 in.

8 in.

8 in.

_____

4.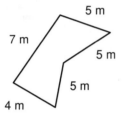

5 m

7 m

5 m

5 m

4 m

_____

5.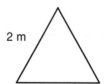

2.3 cm

4.6 cm

_____

6.

1.2 ft

1.2 ft

1.2 ft

1.2 ft

1.2 ft

1.2 ft

_____

Directions Find the perimeter of each regular polygon.

7.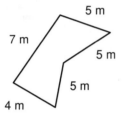

10 in.

_____

8.

2 m

_____

9.

3 ft

_____

Directions The perimeter of each polygon is given. Find the missing length.

10. $P = 43.5$ cm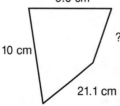

9.0 cm

10 cm

?

21.1 cm

_____

11. $P = 90$ in.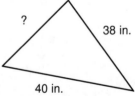

?

38 in.

40 in.

_____

Name _____   Date _____

Parts of Circles

The parts of a circle are described in the chart below.

Part	Description	Example
Center	A point in a plane from which all points of the circle are the same distance	The center is *M*.
Chord	A line segment with endpoints on the circle	$\overline{AB}$ is a chord.
Diameter	A chord that passes through the center of the circle	$\overline{XY}$ is a diameter.
Radius	A line segment with one endpoint at the center of the circle and the other endpoint on the circle	$\overline{MR}$ is a radius.
Arc	A part of a circle between 2 points	$\overparen{CD}$ is an arc.

Directions Refer to the circle at the right to answer 1–5.

1. Name 4 radii. _____

2. Name a diameter. _____

3. Name 2 chords. _____

4. Name the smallest central angle. _____

5. Name 2 arcs that are smaller than $\overparen{BC}$. _____

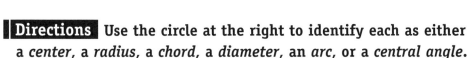

Directions Use the circle at the right to identify each as either
a *center*, a *radius*, a *chord*, a *diameter*, an *arc*, or a *central angle*.

6. $\angle TWU$ _____   **7.** $\overline{VU}$ _____

8. W _____   **9.** $\overparen{ST}$ _____

10. $\angle VWR$ _____   **11.** $\overline{RU}$ _____

12. $\overline{RS}$ _____   **13.** $\overparen{RS}$ _____

Name _____ Date _____

Circumference

The distance around a circle is its **circumference**.

Find the circumference of a circle whose diameter is 8 meters.

$C = \pi d$

$C = 3.14(8)$

$C = 25.12$ m

Find the circumference of a circle whose radius is 3 centimeters.

$C = 2\pi r$

$C = 2(3.14)(3)$

$C = 18.84$ cm

Directions Find each circumference. Use 3.14 for π.

1.

$d = 4$ m

_____

2.

$d = 9$ cm

_____

3.

$r = 5$ cm

_____

4.

$r = 17$ mm

_____

5. $d = 2$ cm

_____

6. $d = 7$ cm

_____

7. $d = 32$ cm

_____

8. $d = 6$ cm

_____

Directions Find each circumference to the nearest tenth. Use 3.14 for π.

9. $d = 4.6$ m

_____

10. $d = 7.3$ cm

_____

11. $d = 8.5$ m

_____

12. $d = 5.4$ cm

_____

13. $r = 2.4$ cm

_____

14. $r = 3.3$ m

_____

15. $r = 8.6$ cm

_____

16. $r = 9.7$ m

_____

Name _____ Date _____

Finding Area

Area of a rectangle
$$A = l \times w$$

Area of a square
$$A = s \times s$$
or
$$A = s^2$$

Directions Find the area of each polygon.

1.
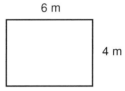
6 m
4 m

_____

2.

7 ft

_____

3.

6 cm
18 cm

_____

Directions Find the area of each rectangle or square.

4. l = 6 in., w = 3 in.

_____

5. l = 12 m, w = 8 m

_____

6. l = 9.4 m, w = 6.7 m

_____

7. s = 7 cm

_____

8. s = 4 yd

_____

9. s = 10 in.

_____

Directions Find the missing side.

10.
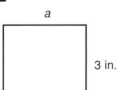
a
3 in.

A = 12 in.^{2}

a = _____

11.
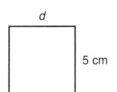
d
5 cm

A = 25 cm^2

d = _____

12.
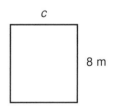
c
8 m

A = 48 m^2

c = _____

Name _____ Date _____

Area of Trapezoids

To find the area of **trapezoid** *ABCD*, we can substitute the values we know into the formula.

$A = \frac{1}{2} h (a + b)$

$A = \frac{1}{2} (2)(2 + 6)$

$A = 8 \text{ cm}^2$

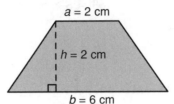

a = 2 cm
h = 2 cm
b = 6 cm

Directions Find the area of each trapezoid.

1.

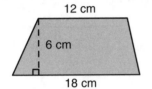

12 cm
6 cm
18 cm

2.

26 cm
14 cm
22 cm

3.

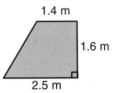

1.4 m
1.6 m
2.5 m

_____   _____   _____

4. $a = 6$ cm, $b = 8$ cm, $h = 7$ cm

5. $a = 2$ cm, $b = 6$ cm, $h = 7$ cm

_____   _____

6. $a = 18$ m, $b = 17$ m, $h = 15$ m

7. $a = 18$ m, $b = 15$ m, $h = 25$ m

_____   _____

8. $a = 4.6$ cm, $b = 5.4$ cm, $h = 2.3$ cm

9. $a = 2.4$ cm, $b = 3.1$ cm, $h = 1.3$ cm

_____   _____

Another way to write the area formula for a trapezoid is

$A = \frac{1}{2} h (b_1 + b_2)$ b_1 is one base, and
b_2 is the other base.

Directions Find the area of each trapezoid.

10. $b_1 = 9$ cm
$b_2 = 11$ cm
$h = 5$ cm

11. $b_1 = 6$ m
$b_2 = 14$ m
$h = 7$ m

12. $b_1 = 24$ cm
$b_2 = 36$ cm
$h = 40$ cm

_____   _____   _____

Name _____   Date _____

Area of Triangles

To find the area of a triangle, multiply $\frac{1}{2}$ times the base times the height.

$$A = \frac{1}{2} \times b \times h \quad \text{or} \quad A = \frac{bh}{2}$$

Directions Find the area.

1.

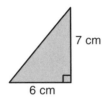

7 cm

6 cm

_____

2.

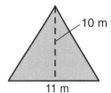

10 m

11 m

_____

3.

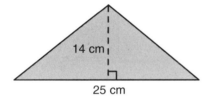

14 cm

25 cm

_____

4.

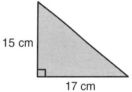

15 cm

17 cm

_____

5.

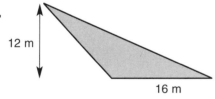

12 m

16 m

_____

Directions The length of the base and the height are given. Find the area of each triangle.

6. $b = 4$ cm, $h = 7$ cm

_____

7. $b = 17$ cm, $h = 16$ cm

_____

8. $b = 3.6$ cm, $h = 2.4$ cm

_____

9. $b = 12.6$ cm, $h = 11.9$ cm

_____

Go on to the next page.

Name _____ Date _____

Area of Triangles, p. 2

To find the area of a triangle, multiply $\frac{1}{2}$ times the length of the base times the height.

$A = \frac{1}{2} \times b \times h$

$A = \frac{1}{2} \times 4 \times 3$

$A = 6$ cm^2

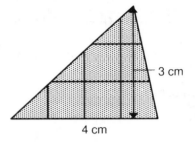

3 cm

4 cm

The area of the triangle is 6 square centimeters.

Directions Find the area of each figure.

1.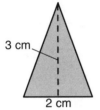

3 cm

2 cm

_____

2.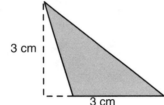

3 cm

3 cm

_____

3.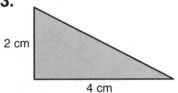

2 cm

4 cm

_____

Directions The base and the height are given. Find the area for each.

4. b = 10 cm, h = 9 cm _____

5. b = 29 cm, h = 12 cm _____

6. b = 8 cm, h = 6 cm _____

7. b = 12 m, h = 5 m _____

8. b = 47 m, h = 20 m _____

9. b = 16 cm, h = 13 cm _____

10. b = 16 cm, h = 9 cm _____

11. b = 65 m, h = 46 m _____

12. b = 46 mm, h = 20 mm _____

Name _____ Date _____

Mixed Areas

Directions Find each area.

1.

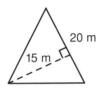

2.

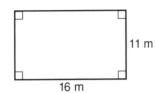

3.

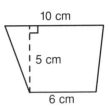

_____

_____

_____

4.

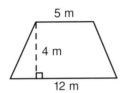

5.

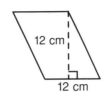

6.

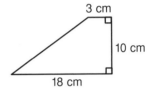

_____

_____

_____

7. Rectangle
l = 3.4 cm
w = 5.9 cm

8. Triangle
b = 5.7 cm
h = 2.2 cm

9. Parallelogram
b = 8.5 m
h = 6.1 m

_____

_____

_____

10. Triangle
b = 6.2 m
h = 4.9 m

11. Parallelogram
b = 16.4 cm
h = 13.9 cm

12. Rectangle
l = 7.7 m
w = 11.9 m

_____

_____

_____

Name _____ Date _____

Area of Circles

You can understand the formula for the area of a circle by cutting a circle into wedges fit together to form a shape that looks like a parallelogram.

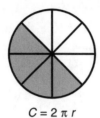

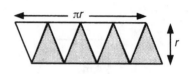

$C = 2\pi r$

The height of the parallelogram is the radius of the circle. The base of the parallelogram is $\frac{1}{2}$ the circumference of the circle. So, the area of the parallelogram can be written as $\pi r \times r$ or πr^2. You can find the area of a circle if you are given its diameter or its radius.

Given	To find the area	Example
Diameter	• Divide the diameter by 2 to find the radius. • Use the formula $A = \pi r^2$.	$d = 14$ m $r = 14 \div 2 = 7$ m $A = \pi \times r^2$ $A = 3.14 \times 7^2$ $A = 3.14 \times 49$ $A = 153.86$ m^2
Radius	• Use the formula $A = \pi r^2$.	$r = 3$ in. $A = \pi \times r^2$ $A = 3.14 \times 3^2$ $A = 3.14 \times 9$ $A = 28.26$ in.^{2}

Directions Find the area of the circle. Use 3.14 for π.

1.

2 cm

_____

2.

4 in.

_____

3.

12 ft

_____

Directions Find the area of each circle. Use 3.14 for π.

4. $r = 8$ m _____

5. $r = 15$ yd _____

6. $r = 24$ ft _____

7. $r = 12$ in. _____

Finding Circles

To find the area of a circle:

$A = \pi r^2$

Remember if the diameter is given, to find the radius, divide the diameter by 2.

$r = \frac{d}{2}$

Directions Find each area. Use 3.14 for π.

1.
2 cm

_____

2.
7 in.

_____

3.
12 m

_____

4.
15 ft

_____

Directions Find each area to the nearest whole number. Use 3.14 for π.

5. $d = 9$ m

_____

6. $d = 2.1$ cm

_____

7. $r = 6.1$ cm

_____

8. $r = 7.3$ mm

_____

9. $d = 56$ m

_____

10. $d = 63$ m

_____

11. $r = 2.8$ cm

_____

12. $r = 4\frac{1}{5}$ cm

_____

Directions Find the area of the shaded region. Use 3.14 for π.

13.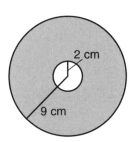
2 cm
9 cm

_____

14.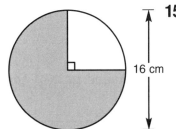
16 cm

_____

15.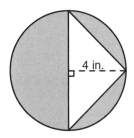
4 in.

_____

Name _____   Date _____

Area of Irregular Figures

Directions Find the area of familiar shapes in Figure A.

1. Into what familiar shapes does the dashed line divide Figure A?

   _____

2. What is the area of each shape?

   _____

3. What is the area of Figure A?

   _____

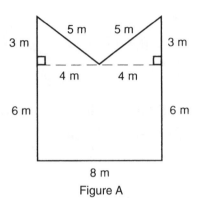

Figure A

Directions Find the area of the shaded part of Figure B.

4. What familiar shapes do you see in Figure B?

   _____

5. How do you find the area of Figure B?

   _____

6. What is the area of the shaded part of Figure B?

   _____

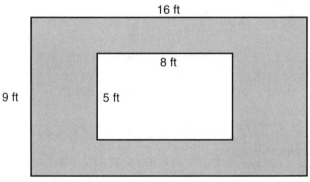

Figure B

Directions Find the area of the shaded part of the figure.

7.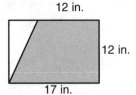

   _____

8.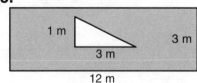

   _____

9.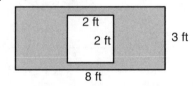

   _____

Name _____   Date _____

Estimating Perimeter and Area

Directions Use estimation for 1–2. Solve 3.

1. Predict which of the 5 polygons have the same perimeter.

_____

2. Predict which of the 5 polygons have the same area.

_____

A

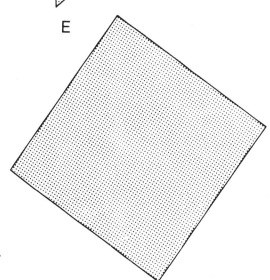

B

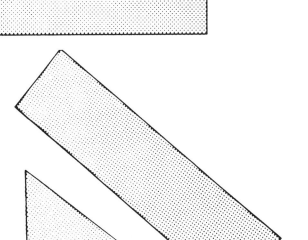

C

D

E

3. Measure each polygon with a centimeter ruler. Find the perimeter
and area of each polygon. Were your answers to 1 and 2 correct?

_____

Unit 3 Assessment

Directions Solve each problem.

1. A 5-gallon can of asphalt sealant covers about 250 square feet. How many cans of sealant are needed to cover a tennis court that is 78 ft by 27 ft?

   _____

2. Jack wants to paint the 4 walls of his bedroom. The room is 24 feet long by 12 feet wide by 8 feet high. If 1 gallon of paint is enough to cover 144 square feet, how many gallons will he need?

   _____

3. The parking lot at the library is rectangular. It has an area of 2,750 m². The width of the parking lot is 55 m. What is the length?

   _____

4. A rug is 10 ft long and 8 ft wide. What is the perimeter of the rug?

   _____

5. The length of a rug is 4 yards. Its width is 3 yards. What is the area of the rug?

   _____

6. The area of a rectangle is 27 cm². If the width is 3 cm, what is the length?

   _____

Directions Identify each part.

7. Scott measured a window opening in the house he is building. The width of the opening is 2 m and the height is 3 m. What is the area of the opening?

   Shape: _____

   Formula: _____

   Solution: _____

8. Miss Eddy wants to cover her bulletin board with blue paper. The board measures 5 ft on each side. How many square feet of paper will Miss Eddy need?

   Shape: _____

   Formula: _____

   Solution: _____

9. For his project, Lewis needs a triangular piece of wood that has a base of 25 cm and a height of 16 cm. How many square centimeters of wood is that?

   Shape: _____

   Formula: _____

   Solution: _____

10. Nora is putting a new floor in her kitchen. If her kitchen is 18 ft by 22 ft, how many square feet of flooring will she need?

    Shape: _____

    Formula: _____

    Solution: _____

Name _____ Date _____

Creative Perimeters

Directions Find a way to separate the rectangle into regions to satisfy the given conditions.

1. Separate this rectangle into 2 regions, each with a perimeter of 8 units.

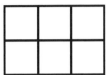

2. Separate this rectangle into 4 regions, each with a perimeter of 10 units.

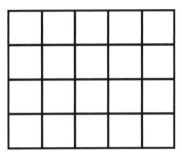

3. Separate this rectangle into 4 regions, each with a perimeter of 12 units.

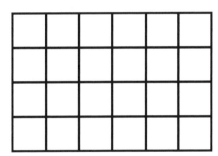

4. Separate this rectangle into 4 regions, each with a perimeter of 8 units.

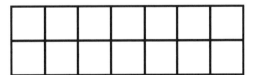

5. Separate this rectangle into 6 regions, each with a perimeter of 10 units.

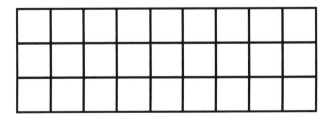

Name _____ Date _____

Perimeter and Area

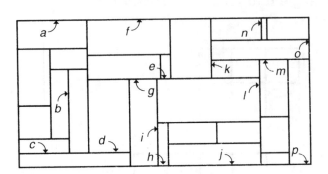

Dimensions (in Number of Units)

a = 10	i = 5
b = 9	j = 13
c = 7	k = 3
d = 4	l = 6
e = 3	m = 2
f = 11	n = 2
g = 3	o = 2
h = 1	p = 2

Directions Follow the steps in 1–10 to find the perimeter
and area of the large rectangle.

1. Find the length of *i*.

_____

2. Find the length of *i* + *l*.

_____

3. Find the length of *k* + *o*.

_____

4. Find the length of (*i* + *l*) + (*k* + *o*) + *n*.

_____

5. Find the width of the large rectangle.

_____

6. Find the length of *g* + *h*.

_____

7. Find the length of (*a* + *d*) + (*g* + *h*) + (*j* + *m*) + *p*.

_____

8. Find the length of the large rectangle.

_____

9. Find the perimeter of the large rectangle.

_____

10. What is the area of the large rectangle?

_____

Tangram Areas

Many puzzles are based on isosceles right triangles. One of the most common is the *tangram puzzle*. In the puzzle are 7 shapes, 4 of which are isosceles right triangles. The 7 pieces can be arranged to make many figures, including a square.

The sides of the large square are 2 inches long. The legs of isosceles triangle 1 are 1 inch long.

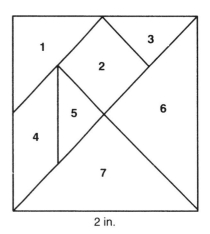

2 in.

Directions Find the dimensions of the tangram pieces. Use inches as the unit of measure. Find their areas.

1.

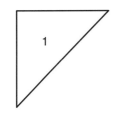

_____

2.

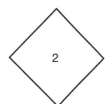

_____

3.

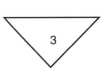

_____

4.

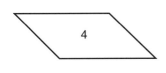

_____

5.

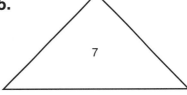

_____

6. Show that the sum of the areas of the 7 pieces equals the area of the square.

_____

Unusual Areas

You can use what you know about the areas of rectangles, parallelograms, triangles, and trapezoids to determine the areas of many unusually shaped plane figures.

Study Figure A, with the dimensions given. Assume the following conditions:

a. The star is symmetrical.

b. The 4 triangular points are congruent.

c. The measures are as shown.

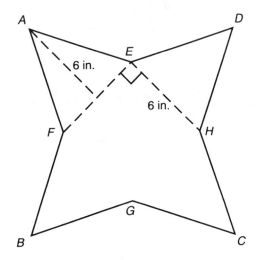

Figure A

Directions Use Figure A to answer 1–3.

1. What is the area of each point?

_____

2. What is the area of the center of the figure?

_____

3. What is the total area of the figure?

_____

Directions Find the total area of these figures. Measurements that you need are given. Assume the conditions given.

4. $\overline{AB} \parallel \overline{CD}$; $\overline{CD}$ = 29 in.; $\overline{CF} = \overline{BG}$

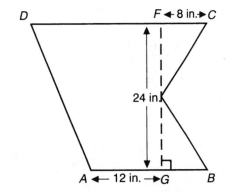

5. The 6 points are congruent isosceles triangles.

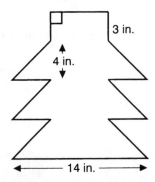

_____   _____

Formulating the Area or Perimeter

The formulas for perimeter, circumference, and area can be used to solve many different problems. Be sure to use the correct formula to solve a given problem. Use 3.14 for π.

Directions Solve using the appropriate formula.

1. A rectangular mat is 9.6 centimeters long and 5.3 centimeters wide. Find the area of the mat.

_____

2. A rectangular flower garden is 3.4 meters long and 2.8 meters wide. What is its perimeter?

_____

3. One side of a square cloth is 28 centimeters. Find the area of the cloth.

_____

4. A circular dartboard has a diameter of 36 centimeters. What is the area of the dartboard?

_____

5. How many 2 in. equilateral triangle cuttings are required for a regular hexagon whose sides each measure 2 in.?

_____

6. How many 2 in. equilateral triangle cuttings are required to complete an equilateral triangle whose sides each measure 8 in.?

_____

Name _____   Date _____

Area and Perimeter Problems

Drawing a diagram can often help you solve a problem. Be sure the diagram shows all the facts you have.

Directions Solve. Draw a diagram if you need help.

1. Frank wants to use a 9 × 12 centimeter frame for a 7 × 10 centimeter picture. In order to make the picture fit, how wide a border should he put on each side of the picture?

   _____

2. Jim is building a rectangular sandbox for his son. He wants it to measure 2 meters by $3\frac{1}{2}$ meters. How many meters of wood will he need?

   _____

3. Jeannette has a 4 × 6 centimeter frame into which she wants to put a 5 × 7 centimeter photo. How much must she trim off each side of the photo?

   _____

4. Paul wants to fence in a square section of land that has a perimeter of 140 meters. If fencing is sold in 5-meter sections, how many sections will he need to buy?

   _____

5. The width of rectangle *ABCD* measures 48 centimeters. If the perimeter is 236 centimeters, how long is rectangle *ABCD*?

   _____

6. The perimeter of square *ABCD* is 104 centimeters. How long is each side?

   _____

7. How many 1 in. square cuttings are required for a 12 in. by 12 in. square exhibit?

   _____

8. How many 4 in. square cuttings are required for an 8 in. by 8 in. square exhibit?

   _____

Shelf Building

Directions Use the picture below to solve each problem.

1. What is the total height of the cabinet?

   _____

2. Can a board that is 3 ft by $1\frac{1}{2}$ ft be used to build the upper shelf?

   _____

3. The back of the cabinet that is behind the doors and drawer will be made of plywood. What are the dimensions of this plywood back?

   _____

4. The back of the cabinet behind the shelves will be made of oak. What are the dimensions of this oak back?

   _____

5. How many $1\frac{1}{4}$ in. books will fit across the lower shelf?

   _____

6. The cabinet has a floor. Blair builds 2 shelves inside the doors. The shelves are spaced evenly inside. How many inches apart are these two shelves?

   _____

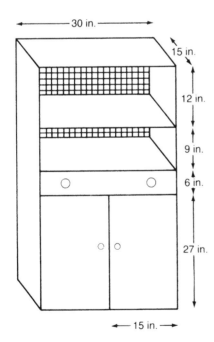

Name _____   Date _____

Using Area and Perimeter

Directions Draw a picture or diagram to help you solve each problem.

1. Mrs. Smollet made a table that has 4 folding leaves. The center of the table is square, and each leaf is a semicircle whose diameter is equal to 1 side of the square. The square is 3 feet per side. What is the area of the table?

   _____

2. Lee is a designer. The sketch that he is working on is a 13 in.-by-15 in. rectangle. One of the 13 in. sides is also the base of a triangle that has a height of 10 in. One of the 15 in. sides is also the base of a triangle that has a height of 12 in. What is the total area of the sketch?

   _____

3. The McGraths' new property is 200 ft long and 75 ft wide. Their previous property was 160 ft long and 80 ft wide. Is the area of the McGraths' new property greater or less than that of their old property? By how much?

   _____

4. Milo has a round vegetable garden enclosed by a low, square wall. The wall is 25 feet to a side. What is the area of the vegetable garden?

   _____

5. In front of an office building there is a round pond that has a flower garden around it. The diameter of the entire garden is 37 feet. The diameter of the pond is 5 feet. What is the area of the garden around the pond?

   _____

6. A large sculpture in North Shore Seaport's town square is triangular in shape. Its area is 6,405 ft². Its base is 61 ft wide. A similar sculpture in South Shore has an area of 11,505 ft² and a base that is 59 ft wide. How much taller is the sculpture in South Shore than the one in North Shore?

   _____

Name _____ Date _____

More Areas and Perimeters

Directions Draw a picture or diagram to help you solve each problem. Use 3.14 for π. Round to the nearest hundredth.

1. Outside the Kelly Museum, there are 2 gardens: 1 circular and the other square. The distance between the centers of the gardens is 78 feet. The circular garden has a diameter of 20 feet. Each side of the square garden is 54.6 feet. How many feet apart are the 2 gardens?

_____

2. Lars is walking around a path in the park. He walks 50 feet north, 40 feet east, 20 feet south, and 60 feet west. How long is the path around the park?

_____

3. Portia is enlarging a triangular garden. The original garden has a base of 15 feet and a height of 12 feet. Portia increases the height by 4 feet and the base by 8 feet. How much larger is the new garden?

_____

4. The centers of 3 circles lie along the same straight line. The circles have radii of 12 in., 16 in., and 25 in., in that order. If the sides of the circles are touching, how far is the center of the first circle from the center of the last?

_____

5. Teddy is painting a mural of an ice cream cone. The cone is a triangle that has a height of 25 feet and a base of 12.5 feet. The ice cream is a semicircle that sits on the base of the triangle. What is the total area of the mural?

_____

Circles in Squares

Directions Find the answer to the nearest square centimeter.

1. One circle with a 12-centimeter radius fits over this
   square. The area of the square is how much
   greater than the area of the circle?

   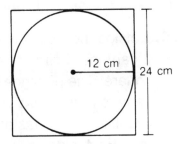

   _____

2. Four circles, each with a 6-centimeter radius, fit
   over the square. The area of the square is how
   much greater than the combined areas of the
   circles?

   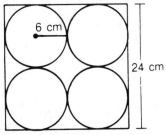

   _____

3. Nine circles, each with a 4-centimeter radius, fit
   over the square. The area of the square is how
   much greater than the combined areas of
   the circles?

   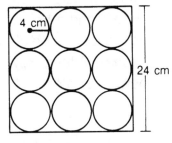

   _____

4. How many circles with a 3-centimeter radius will
   fit over the square?

   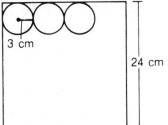

   _____

5. The area of the square is how much greater
   than the combined areas of the circles with
   3-centimeter radii?

   _____

6. How many circles with a 2-centimeter radius will fit
   over the square?

   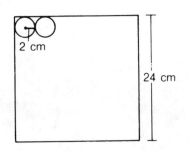

   _____

Tangrams

The 5 small polygons at the bottom of the page can be put together to form many different shapes. Cut them out.

Directions Use all 5 of your small polygons to form each of the large polygons in 1–4. Draw in the shapes to show how they fit together.

1.

2.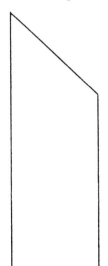

3.

4.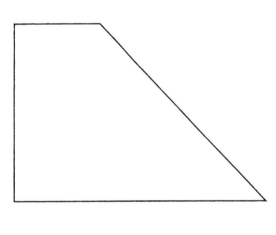

Name _____ Date _____

Pi Wrapping

Directions Work in pairs to complete this worksheet.

- Select 3 pieces of string with varying lengths to be used as radii.
- Select 1 long piece of string for measuring the circumference.
- Choose a piece of chalk or a crayon.
- Tie 1 end of the string around the chalk or crayon.
- Have a ruler available.

On the chalkboard or a piece of paper, you will draw 3 different circles, using the string pieces you have chosen as the radius for each of 3 circles.

- One person holds the end of the string without the chalk by pressing down on the drawing surface being used.
- The other person, holding the chalk and keeping the string taut, draws a circle.
- Repeat to draw circles *A, B, C*.
- Use the ruler to draw and measure each diameter.
- Wrap the long piece of string around the circle to measure the circumference.
- Next, lay the long piece of string along the diameter repeatedly to see how many lengths of diameter are in the circumference.
- Finally, find the ratio of the measure of the circumference to the measure of the diameter.
- Complete the table.

Circle	Length of Diameter	Length of Circumference	Diameter Lengths in Circumference	Circumference ÷ Diameter
A				
B				
C				

Define *pi* using information from your experiment.

_____

_____

Name _____   Date _____

Revolutions

Suppose you make a mark at the edge of an automobile tire. If the automobile moves forward until the mark comes back to its original position, the automobile will have moved forward a distance equal to the circumference of the tire.

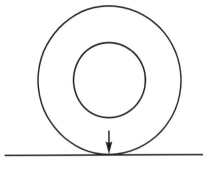

A tire on an automobile has a radius of 12 inches. How far will the automobile move in 1 revolution of the tire?

Write the formula. ⟶ $C = 2\pi r$

Substitute the numbers. ⟶ $C = 2 \times 3.14 \times 12$

Compute. ⟶ $C = 75.36$

The automobile will travel about 75 inches.

Directions **Solve. Round your answer to the nearest whole number.**

1. An automobile tire has a radius of 13 inches. How far will the automobile travel if the tire revolves 1 time?

   _____

2. An automobile tire has a radius of 14 inches. How far will the automobile travel if the tire revolves 3 times?

   _____

3. If a tire has a radius of 12 inches, how many times must the tire revolve to move the vehicle 530 inches?

   _____

4. If a tire has a radius of 13 inches, how many times must the tire revolve to move the vehicle 100 feet?

   _____

5. Ms. Thomas drives 3 miles to school. If the tires on her car have a radius of 12 inches, how many times do they revolve in 1 trip to school?

   _____

6. Mr. Averez takes a business trip of 120 miles. If the tires on his car have a radius of 14 inches, how many times will they revolve during his trip?

   _____

Combination of Perimeters

Directions Find the perimeter of the figure to the nearest whole centimeter.

Step One   Find the sum of the lengths of the
three sides of the rectangle.
14 + 14 + 8 = 36

Step Two   Find half the circumference of
the circle.
(3.14 × 8) ÷ 2 = 12.56

Step Three   Add the answers and round to
the nearest whole number.
36 + 12.56 = 48.56 = 49

The perimeter is about 49 cm.

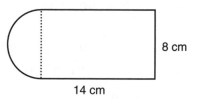

Directions Find the perimeter. Round your answers to the nearest whole centimeter.

1.

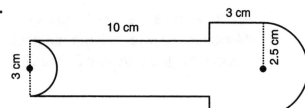

_____

2.

_____

3.

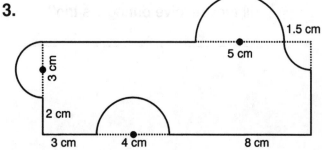

_____

Name _____   Date _____

Perimeters to Find Areas

Each edge of each box is a whole number of centimeters in length. The perimeters of 3 faces of each box are given.

Directions Find the dimensions and the areas of the labeled faces.

1.

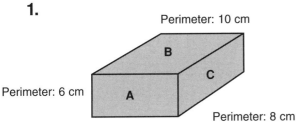

Perimeter: 10 cm
Perimeter: 6 cm
Perimeter: 8 cm

Area of face **A**: _____

Area of face **B**: _____

Area of face **C**: _____

2.

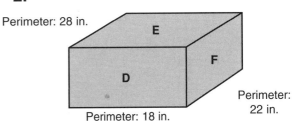

Perimeter: 28 in.
Perimeter: 18 in.
Perimeter: 22 in.

Area of face **D**: _____

Area of face **E**: _____

Area of face **F**: _____

3.

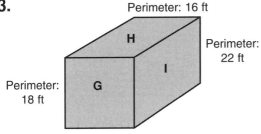

Perimeter: 16 ft
Perimeter: 22 ft
Perimeter: 18 ft

Area of face **G**: _____

Area of face **H**: _____

Area of face **I** : _____

4.

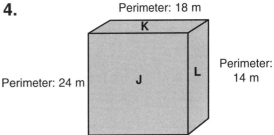

Perimeter: 18 m
Perimeter: 24 m
Perimeter: 14 m

Area of face **J**: _____

Area of face **K**: _____

Area of face **L**: _____

Middle School Geometry: Polygons

Answer Key

Pp. 1–2
1. square, **2.** triangle, **3.** hexagon, **4.** trapezoid, **5.** 10 ft, **6.** 46 m, **7.** 144 in., **8.** C, **9.** $\overline{DE}$, **10.** $\overline{DC}$; $\overline{EC}$; $\overline{FC}$, **11.** $\overline{DE}$; $\overline{AB}$, **12.** 75.36 in., **13.** 37.68 cm, **14.** 18.84 in., **15.** 64 m², **16.** 45 m², **17.** 1,971 m², **18.** 84 ft², **19.** 50.24 in.², **20.** 3,531 yd², **21.** 16 cm², **22.** 12.56 cm², **23.** 2 cm, **24.** 3.44 cm², **25.** 180 ft²; $239.00

P. 3
1. FECB, **2.** ABEF, **3.** ABF; EFB; BCE; BED; DCE, **4.** FECA; AFED; FEDB, **5.** 28 m, **6.** 55 m, **7.** 12.56 cm, **8.** 628 m, **9.** 21.98 ft, **10.** 34.54 in., **11.** 600 ft², **12.** 180 cm², **13.** 384 ft²

P. 4
1. hexagon, **2.** triangle, **3.** rhombus, **4.** trapezoid, **5.** c; f, **6.** a, **7.** a; e, **8.** b; d; also a and e

P. 5
1. no, **2.** no, **3.** no, **4.** yes, **5.** no, **6.** yes, **7.** yes, **8.** yes, **9.** yes; octagon, **10.** no, **11.** yes; decagon, **12.** no, **13.** yes; pentagon, **14.** yes; triangle, **15.** no, **16.** yes; hexagon

P. 6
1. $\overline{ZY}$, **2.** $\overline{PN}$; $\overline{LP}$; $\overline{PN}$; $\overline{LP}$. **3.** $\overline{TV}$; $\overline{VW}$; $\overline{SW}$, **4.** 90; 90; 90; 90, **5.** $\overline{KL}$; $\overline{LM}$; $\overline{MJ}$, **6.** FECB, **7.** ABEF, **8.** FECA; AFED; FEDB

P. 7
1. quadrilateral; parallelogram; rectangle; square; rhombus, **2.** quadrilateral; trapezoid, **3.** quadrilateral, **4.** quadrilateral; parallelogram; rectangle, **5.** quadrilateral; parallelogram, **6.** quadrilateral; parallelogram; rhombus

P. 8
1. 100 cm, **2.** 117 cm, **3.** 160 mm, **4.** 125 cm, **5.** 164 cm, **6.** 168 mm, **7.** 55 m, **8.** 24 in., **9.** 28 ft

P. 9
1. 34 mm, **2.** 43.2 m, **3.** 35.2 cm, **4.** 38.6 cm, **5.** 13.1 m, **6.** 180 cm, **7.** 23 m, **8.** 262.4 cm, **9.** 512 cm, **10.** 32.8 m, **11.** 109.6 cm, **12.** 26.8 m

P. 10
1. P, **2.** $\overline{ML}$; $\overline{NQ}$, **3.** 1/2 in., **4.** 1/2 in., **5.** 1 in., **6.** 1/2 in., **7.** A, **8.** $\overline{AB}$; $\overline{AH}$; $\overline{AE}$, **9.** $\overline{CD}$; $\overline{EH}$; $\overline{FG}$, **10.** ∠BAH, **11.** ∠BAE

P. 11
1. a little more than 3 times longer, **2.** Answers may vary.; yes, **3.** 9.42 in., **4.** 125.6 cm, **5.** 56.52 cm, **6.** 132 in., **7.** 44 mm, **8.** 56 4/7 in.

P. 12
1. 18.84 m, **2.** 75.36 cm, **3.** 56.52 mm, **4.** 12.56 cm, **5.** 28.26 in., **6.** 94.2 m, **7.** 44 in., **8.** 132 mm, **9.** 88 cm, **10.** 88 in., **11.** 44 cm, **12.** 132 ft

P. 13
1. 15 cm², **2.** 4 cm², **3.** 4 cm², **4.** 21 cm², **5.** 32 mm², **6.** 45 cm², **7.** 168 m², **8.** 36 cm², **9.** 64 mm², **10.** 4 m², **11.** 25 m²

P. 14
1. 96 cm², **2.** 30 in.², **3.** 81 ft², **4.** 24 cm², **5.** 60 m², **6.** 36 in²

P. 15
1. A = s², **2.** A = b × h, **3.** A = l × w, **4.** 16 m², **5.** 38.44 m², **6.** 201.64 m², **7.** 219.6 mm², **8.** 6.29 in², **9.** 1,134 in.², **10.** 180 cm², **11.** 119.28 ft², **12.** 352 m²

P. 16
1. 16 in., **2.** 135 m, **3.** 28.26 in., **4.** 31.40 in., **5.** 81 m², **6.** 81 ft², **7.** 24 m², **8.** 28.26 in.², **9.** 105 cm², **10.** 60 m²

P. 17
1. rhombus; parallelogram, **2.** trapezoid, **3.** rectangle; parallelogram, **4.** parallelogram, **5.** rhombus; parallelogram, **6.** square; rhombus, also parallelogram; rectangle, **7.** square; rectangle, **8.** trapezoid, **9.** $\overline{AB} \parallel \overline{DC}$; $\overline{AD} \parallel \overline{BC}$, **10.** $\overline{EF} \parallel \overline{HG}$, **11.** $\overline{IJ} \parallel \overline{LK}$; $\overline{IL} \parallel \overline{JK}$, **12.** $\overline{MN} \parallel \overline{PO}$; $\overline{MP} \parallel \overline{NO}$, **13.** $\overline{QR} \parallel \overline{ST}$; $\overline{QT} \parallel \overline{RS}$, **14.** $\overline{UV} \parallel \overline{WX}$; $\overline{XU} \parallel \overline{WV}$, **15.** $\overline{BC} \parallel \overline{DE}$; $\overline{CD} \parallel \overline{BE}$, **16.** $\overline{FG} \parallel \overline{IH}$

P. 18
1. 26, **2.** 23, **3.** 18, **4.** 378, **5.** 6, **6.** 24

P. 19
1. 12 m, **2.** 22 cm, **3.** 32 mm, **4.** 48 cm, **5.** 38 m, **6.** 76 mm, **7.** 84 cm, **8.** 24 m

P. 20
1. 12.26 m, **2.** 13.4 yd, **3.** 32 in., **4.** 26 m, **5.** 13.8 cm, **6.** 7.2 ft, **7.** 40 in., **8.** 6 m, **9.** 18 ft, **10.** 3.4 cm, **11.** 12 in.

P. 21
1. $\overline{AX}$; $\overline{BX}$; $\overline{CX}$; $\overline{DX}$, **2.** $\overline{AD}$, **3.** $\overline{BC}$; $\overline{AD}$, **4.** ∠DXC, **5.** $\overline{AB}$; $\overline{CD}$, **6.** central angle, **7.** chord, **8.** center, **9.** arc, **10.** central angle, **11.** diameter or chord, **12.** chord, **13.** arc

P. 22
1. 12.56 m, **2.** 28.26 cm, **3.** 31.4 cm, **4.** 106.76 mm, **5.** 6.28 cm, **6.** 21.98 cm, **7.** 100.48 cm, **8.** 18.84 cm, **9.** 14.4 m, **10.** 22.9 cm, **11.** 26.7 m, **12.** 17.0 cm, **13.** 15.1 cm, **14.** 20.7 m, **15.** 54.0 cm, **16.** 60.9 m

P. 23
1. 24 m², **2.** 49 ft², **3.** 108 cm², **4.** 18 in.², **5.** 96 m², **6.** 62.98 m², **7.** 49 cm², **8.** 16 yd², **9.** 100 in.², **10.** a = 4 in., **11.** d = 5 cm, **12.** c = 6 m

P. 24
1. 90 cm², **2.** 336 cm², **3.** 3.12 m², **4.** 49 cm², **5.** 28 cm², **6.** 262.5 m², **7.** 412.5 m², **8.** 11.5 cm², **9.** 3.575 cm², **10.** 50 cm², **11.** 70 m², **12.** 1,200 cm²

P. 25
1. 21 cm², **2.** 55 m², **3.** 175 cm², **4.** 127.5 cm², **5.** 96 m², **6.** 14 cm², **7.** 136 cm², **8.** 4.32 cm², **9.** 74.97 cm²

P. 26
1. 3 cm², **2.** 4.5 cm², **3.** 4 cm², **4.** 45 cm², **5.** 174 cm², **6.** 24 cm², **7.** 30 m², **8.** 470 m², **9.** 104 cm², **10.** 72 cm², **11.** 1,495 m², **12.** 460 mm²

P. 27
1. 34 m², **2.** 144 cm², **3.** 40 cm², **4.** 150 m², **5.** 176 m², **6.** 105 cm², **7.** 20.06 cm², **8.** 6.27 cm², **9.** 51.85 m², **10.** 15.19 m², **11.** 227.96 cm², **12.** 91.63 m²

P. 28
1. 12.56 cm², **2.** 50.24 in.², **3.** 113.04 ft², **4.** 200.96 m², **5.** 706.5 yd², **6.** 1,808.64 ft², **7.** 452.16 in.²

P. 29
1. 3.14 cm², **2.** 153.86 in.², **3.** 113.04 m², **4.** 706.5 ft², **5.** 64 m², **6.** 3 cm², **7.** 117 cm², **8.** 167 mm², **9.** 2,462 m², **10.** 3,116 m², **11.** 25 cm², **12.** 55 cm², **13.** 241.78 cm², **14.** 150.72 cm², **15.** 34.24 in.²

P. 30
1. 2 triangles and a rectangle, **2.** triangles = 6 m² each; rectangle = 48 m², **3.** 60 m², **4.** rectangles, **5.** Subtract the area of the smaller inner rectangle from the area of the larger rectangle., **6.** 104 ft², **7.** 174 in.², **8.** 34.5 m², **9.** 20 ft²

P. 31
1. Answers may vary slightly. Polygons A and C have about the same perimeter., **2.** Answers may vary slightly. Polygons A and D have about the same area., **3.** Answers will vary.

P. 32
1. 9, **2.** 4, **3.** 50 m, **4.** 36 ft, **5.** 12 yd², **6.** 9 cm, **7.** rectangle; A = l × w; 6 m², **8.** square; A = s²; 25 ft², **9.** triangle; A = 1/2(b x h); 200 cm², **10.** rectangle; A = l x w; 396 ft²

P. 33
Answers will vary. Check students' work.

P. 34
1. 5, **2.** 11, **3.** 5, **4.** 18, **5.** 14, **6.** 4, **7.** 35, **8.** 38, **9.** 104, **10.** 532

P. 35
Answers may vary slightly.
1. 1/2 in.², **2.** 9/16 in.², **3.** 9/32 in.², **4.** 1/2 in.², **5.** 1 in.²

P. 36
1. 18 in.², **2.** 36 in.², **3.** 108 in.², **4.** 492 in.², **5.** 138 in.²

P. 37
1. 50.88 cm², **2.** 12.4 m, **3.** 784 cm², **4.** 1,017.36 cm², **5.** 6, **6.** 16

P. 38
1. 1 cm, **2.** 11 m, **3.** 1/2 cm, **4.** 28 sections, **5.** 70 cm, **6.** 26 cm, **7.** 144, **8.** 4

P. 39
1. 54 in., **2.** yes, **3.** 33 in. high by 30 in. wide, **4.** 21 in. high by 30 in. wide, **5.** 24 books, **6.** 9 in.

P. 40
1. 23.13 ft², **2.** 350 in.², **3.** 2,200 ft² greater, **4.** 490.625 ft², **5.** 1,055.04 ft², **6.** 180 ft

P. 41
1. 40.7 ft, **2.** 170 ft, **3.** 94 ft² larger, **4.** 69 in., **5.** 217.58 ft²

P. 42
1. 124 cm², **2.** 124 cm², **3.** 124 cm², **4.** 16, **5.** 124 cm², **6.** 36

P. 43
Check students' work.

P. 44
Answers will vary. Check students' work.

P. 45
1. 82 in., **2.** 264 in., **3.** 7 times, **4.** 15 times, **5.** 2,522 times, **6.** 86,479 times

P. 46
1. 41 cm, **2.** 46 cm, **3.** 46 cm.

P. 47
1. A = 2 cm²; B = 6 cm²; C = 3 cm²; D = 18 in.²; E = 48 in.²; F = 24 in.², **3.** G = 18 ft²; H = 15 ft²; I = 30 ft², **4.** J = 35 m²; K = 14 m²; L = 10 m²